NO MORE DEAD

Fairmont School Dist. #89
735 Green Garden Place
Lockport, IL 60441

by
Gordon Korman

Student Packet

Written by
Sharan Farmer

Contains masters for:

2 Prereading Activities
7 Vocabulary Activities
1 Study Guide
4 Literary Analysis Activities
2 Character Analysis Activities
1 Critical Thinking Activity
4 Quizzes
1 Novel Test

PLUS Detailed Answer Key
and Scoring Rubric

Note

The Hyperion Paperbacks for Children edition of the book, ©2000 by Gordon Korman, was used to prepare this guide. Page references may differ in other editions. Novel ISBN: 0-7868-1601-5

Please note: Please assess the appropriateness of this book for the age level and maturity of your students prior to reading and discussing it with them

---

ISBN-10: 1-58130-947-3
ISBN-13: 978-1-58130-947-8

Copyright infringement is a violation of Federal Law.

© 2006 by Novel Units, Inc., Bulverde, Texas. All rights reserved. No part of this publication may be reproduced, translated, stored in a retrieval system, or transmitted in any way or by any means (electronic, mechanical, photocopying, recording, or otherwise) without prior written permission from ECS Learning Systems, Inc.

Photocopying of student worksheets by a classroom teacher at a non-profit school who has purchased this publication for his/her own class is permissible. Reproduction of any part of this publication for an entire school or for a school system, by for-profit institutions and tutoring centers, or for commercial sale is strictly prohibited.

Novel Units is a registered trademark of ECS Learning Systems, Inc.
Printed in the United States of America.

To order, contact your local school supply store, or—
Novel Units, Inc.
P.O. Box 97
Bulverde, TX 78163-0097

Web site: www.novelunits.com

Lori Mammen, Editorial Director
Andrea M. Harris, Production Manager/Production Specialist
Taylor Henderson, Product Development Specialist
Heather M. Marnan, Product Development Specialist
Suzanne K. Mammen, Curriculum Specialist
Pamela Rayfield, Product Development Specialist
Jill Reed, Product Development Specialist
Adrienne Speer, Production Specialist

Anticipation Guide

Directions: Rate each of the following quotations before you read the novel and discuss your ratings with a partner. After you have completed the novel, rate and discuss the quotations again.

1 ——————— 2 ——————— 3 ——————— 4 ——————— 5 ——————— 6

strongly agree   strongly disagree

	Before	After
1. "Honesty is the best policy. If I lose mine honor, I lose myself." *William Shakespeare, playwright*	_____	_____
2. "If you truly want honesty, don't ask questions you don't really want the answer to." *Proverb*	_____	_____
3. "Honesty is the first chapter in the book of wisdom." *Thomas Jefferson, United States President*	_____	_____
4. "No legacy is so rich as honesty." *William Shakespeare, playwright*	_____	_____
5. "Honesty is for the most part less profitable than dishonesty." *Plato, philosopher*	_____	_____
6. "It is hard to believe that a man is telling the truth when you know that you would lie if you were in his place." *Henry Louis Mencken, writer*	_____	_____
7. "A half truth is a whole lie." *Proverb*	_____	_____
8. "We tell lies when we are afraid...afraid of what we don't know, afraid of what others will think, afraid of what will be found out about us. But every time we tell a lie, the thing that we fear grows stronger." *Tad Williams, writer*	_____	_____
9. "People who are brutally honest get more satisfaction out of the brutality than out of the honesty." *Richard J. Needham, writer*	_____	_____
10. "I am different from Washington; I have a higher, grander standard of principle. Washington could not lie. I can lie, but I won't." *Mark Twain, writer*	_____	_____

All rights reserved

Character Analysis

Directions: Working in small groups, discuss the attributes of the types of characters listed in the top row of boxes. In each box, write several words or phrases that describe how this type of character is generally viewed. After reading the novel, label the oval under each box in the bottom row with the names of major characters from the novel who fit these roles. Discuss if that character has the traits described in the top row. In the boxes, write words or phrases that show how each character does or does not fit the typical stereotype as described above.

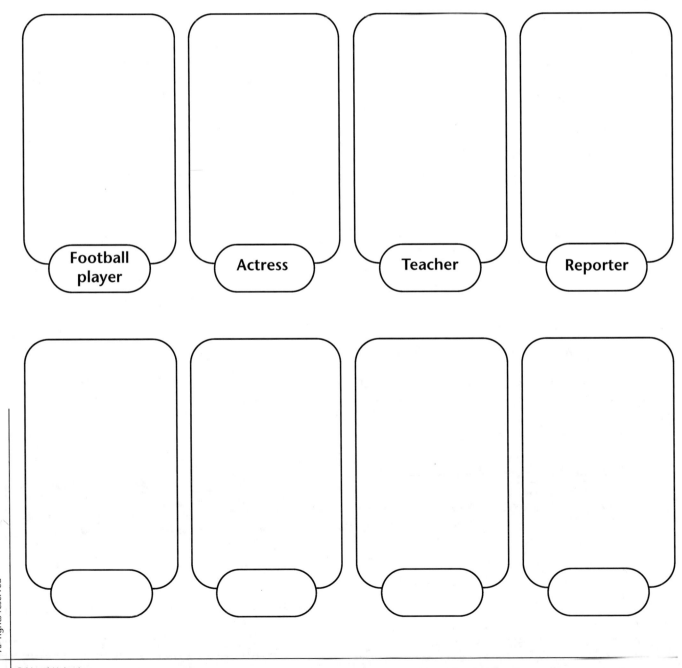

Football player　　Actress　　Teacher　　Reporter

All rights reserved

Word Map

percolated (2)	slant (3)	toupee (3)	fluke (7)
titan (7)	mediocre (7)	grueling (8)	bamboozled (9)
earnestly (17)	intoned (19)		

Directions: Complete a word map for at least five of the vocabulary words above.

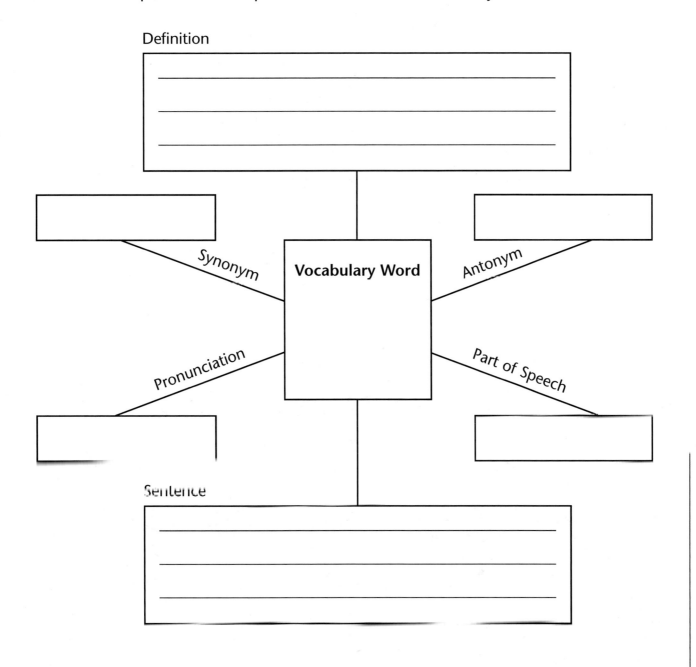

Definition

Synonym

Vocabulary Word

Antonym

Pronunciation

Part of Speech

Sentence

All rights reserved

Name _____

Vocabulary Chart

mulling (21)	reverie (25)	mobbed (26)	uncanny (27)
chortled (28)	hyperventilating (41)	calisthenics (41)	ruckus (44)
snarl (45)			

Directions: Write each vocabulary word in the chart under the proper part of speech as used in the novel. Then write five sentences, using two different vocabulary words in each sentence. Words may be used more than once.

Noun	Verb	Adjective/Adverb	Other

1. _____

2. _____

3. _____

4. _____

5. _____

All rights reserved

sabotage (50)	wheeze (51)	winced (52)	crimson (54)
queasy (55)	clammy (57)	berserk (58)	subdued (58)
reign (60)	pandemonium (60)	affable (60)	strident (60)
epidemic (67)			

Directions: An analogy compares two pairs of words that have similar relationships. For example, BEAR is to FUR as BIRD is to FEATHER. A bear has fur on its body as a bird has feathers on its body. Complete the analogies below choosing a word from the vocabulary list to fill in the blank. Then use four of the remaining words to create your own analogies.

1. ARTIST is to DRAW as KING is to _____.

2. BLUE is to AZURE as RED is to _____.

3. COLOSSAL is to PETITE as ORDERLY is to _____.

4. THIEF is to ROBBER as AMIABLE is to _____.

5. ROLLERCOASTERS are to _____ as NIGHTMARES are to SCARED.

6. WHISPER is to SOFT as SCREECH is to _____.

7. _____ is to _____ as _____ is to _____.

8. _____ is to _____ as _____ is to _____.

9. _____ is to _____ as _____ is to _____.

10. _____ is to _____ as _____ is to _____.

All rights reserved

Name _____

Vocabulary Tic Tac Toe Game

bellowed (73)	sourly (73)	skulking (76)	clambered (80)
snickered (80)	perplexed (82)	ominously (83)	retorted (85)
raved (86)	peevishly (87)	barged (88)	corridor (90)
ricocheted (91)	bickering (93)	cringe (94)	

Directions: Choose nine vocabulary words from the list to fill in the nine squares of the Tic Tac Toe game board below. When a definition is read that matches a word in a square, place a token on it. When you get three in a row in any direction, you win the game.

All rights reserved

Name _____ _____

Vocabulary Card Game

Teacher Directions:
- Photocopy and cut out the following pages.
- Give one card to each student in the class.
- The student who has the starred card begins by reading his/her question.
- The student who has the card with the correct vocabulary word responds and then reads his/her question.
- Play continues in this manner until all cards have been read.

☆ **plagued**

Who has a word that means all eyes focused on something?

fixated

Who has a word that means throwing about?

flailing

Who has a word that means imperative?

urgent

Who has a word that suggests disorder or confusion?

mayhem

Who has a word that means to push forward?

propel

Who has a word that means enjoyed?

All rights reserved

savored ------------------------------------ Who has a word that means affected by something painful?	**stricken** ------------------------------------ Who has a word that means to smile with contempt?
sneer ------------------------------------ Who has a word that represents a reddish-brown color?	**auburn** ------------------------------------ Who has a word that means pitiful?
pathetic ------------------------------------ Who has a word that means to coax?	**wheedle** ------------------------------------ Who has a word that means the opposite of composed?

flustered

Who has a word that means troubled?

All rights reserved

Vocabulary Poems

mortified (124)	mystified (125)	sidled (125)	glowered (127)
bedlam (129)	cram (129)	cowering (132)	ushered (133)
mellow (134)	melancholy (141)	sulked (144)	bailed (144)
incensed (147)			

Directions: A diamante is a seven-line poem that flows from one idea to its opposite.

- Choose two words that are opposites.
- Put the first word (word A) on line 1 and the second word (word B) on line 7.
- On line 2, write 2 adjectives describing A, and on line 6, write 2 adjectives describing B.
- Fill line 3 with 3 verbs ending in "-ing" or "-ed" which are related to A.
- Do the same for line 5, but choose verbs related to B.
- On line 4, write 2 nouns related to A and 2 nouns related to B.

  With a partner, write a diamante including one of the vocabulary words listed above. Be sure to put the vocabulary word on the correct line according to its part of speech. Choose two other vocabulary words to include in two more diamantes.

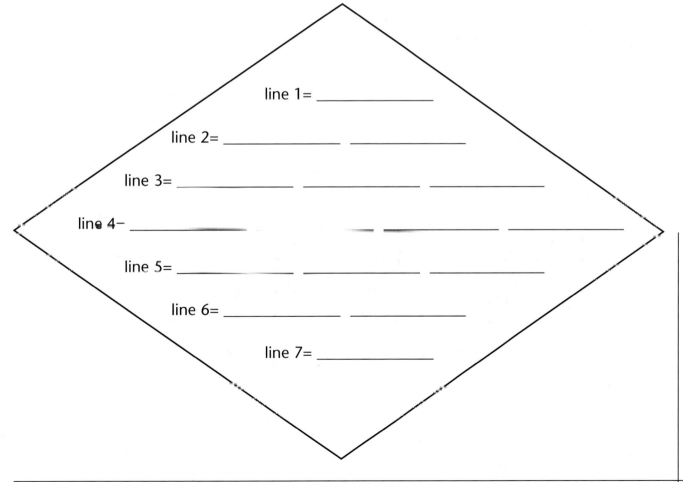

line 1= _____

line 2= _____ _____

line 3= _____ _____ _____

line 4— _____ _____ _____

line 5= _____ _____ _____

line 6= _____ _____

line 7= _____

All rights reserved

Crossword Puzzle

careening (160)	riling (161)	seethed (162)	riffled (164)
mesmerized (169)	plume (170)	mirth (172)	adulation (172)
enraptured (172)	detonated (175)	canine (176)	guffawed (179)

Directions: Select ten vocabulary words from above. Create a crossword puzzle answer key by filling in the grid below. Be sure to number the squares for each word. Blacken any spaces not used by the letters. Then, write clues to the crossword puzzle. Number the clues to match the numbers in the squares. The teacher will give each student a blank grid. Make a blank copy of your crossword puzzle for other students to answer. Exchange your clues with someone else and solve the blank puzzle s/he gives you. Check the completed puzzles with the answer keys.

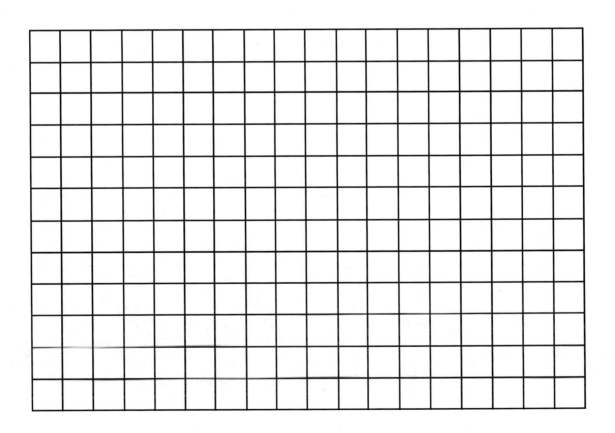

All rights reserved

Directions: Write a brief answer to each question as you read the novel at home or in class. Use the questions to guide your reading, prepare for class discussions, and review for quizzes and the test.

Pages 1–19

1. What does Wallace think is the best policy?
2. What is the name of the novel that Wallace is reviewing?
3. Why doesn't Wallace like the book?
4. Where do Wallace and his friends go to school?
5. Whom does Wallace consider the best player on the football team?
6. Why can't Wallace practice in the evening?
7. To whom does Rachel write fan letters?
8. What is the name of the play that Mr. Fogelman is directing?
9. What does Mr. Fogelman tell Wallace is missing from his second attempt at writing a review?
10. Why is Dylan excited when he meets his sister after school?

Pages 20–45

1. What does Wallace's mom suggest he do to get out of detention?
2. What does Wallace's mom say has been getting him into trouble?
3. What does Coach Wrigley say has been getting Wallace into trouble?
4. What is the one position that Parker Schmidt does not serve on the school newspaper?
5. What three things does Parker claim are the reasons for the "big cover-up" (p. 29)?
6. What is spray-painted on the top of the wooden scenery board?
7. Whom do the drama club members think vandalized the set?
8. What reasons does Trudi give for having a crush on Wallace?
9. Which cast member does not think Wallace's suggestions are so great?
10. What is the second incident of vandalism on the set?

Pages 46–70

1. By how much are the Giants losing each game?
2. Where does Wallace think he belongs on the football team?
3. What does Wallace recruit Rick and Feather to help him do?

All rights reserved

4. What are the three reasons Cavanaugh gives that point to Wallace as the prime suspect of the play vandalism?

5. What does Trudi do to prove Wallace's innocence or guilt?

6. Why is Wallace helping the cast members with their lines?

7. What does Rachel believe is Wallace's real plan for helping the cast?

8. Where does Rachel's family go to celebrate her mom's birthday?

9. In Rachel's letter to Julia Roberts, to what actor does Rachel compare Wallace?

10. What prop does Wallace have Vito use in his revised script?

11. What does Wallace say is the biggest problem with the play?

12. What does Coach Wrigley mean when he tells Mr. Fogelman, "That parking lot is paved with the bones of teachers who are still waiting for Wallace to see it their way" (p. 63)?

13. What is the third act of vandalism on the set?

14. What does Wallace do to help during the pepper prank?

Pages 71–97

1. How does everyone in the stadium learn that Wallace is at Saturday's game?

2. Why does Cavanaugh call Wallace by his real name and not "some nasty double nickname" (p. 74) while in the locker room?

3. What does Wallace see in Feather's locker?

4. What reason does Feather give Wallace for it being in his locker?

5. Besides Feather, who else does Wallace suspect as the vandal?

6. How does Parker describe Wallace in his story?

7. What does Wallace ask the team to help him do?

8. How many members of the team show up to help Wallace?

9. What does Wallace ask Laszlo Tamas to do in the play and why?

10. Whom does Trudi blame for the vandalism and why?

11. What talent does Rory Piper offer to the play?

12. How does Wallace cast Rory?

13. What is the fourth act of vandalism against the play?

14. What is the reaction to the rehearsal of the play's first scene with the moped and Rollerblades?

15. Who or what are the Dead Mangoes?

All rights reserved

Name _____

Pages 98–122

1. Whom does Parker blame for the Giants' losing season?
2. In the previous section, Mr. Fogelman made a memo to do something drastic, and fast. What does he do?
3. How long has Wallace been in detention with Mr. Fogelman?
4. Name two things Wallace likes about Rachel.
5. What is the fifth act of vandalism?
6. Who are Wallace's prime suspects?
7. What does Wallace do to surprise everyone?
8. What "teeny little slipup" (p. 111) does Trudi make?
9. How does Wallace change the role of the vet?
10. What is Mr. Fogelman now contributing to the play?
11. Where are the drama club members going on Saturday?

Pages 123–150

1. What is the difference between the drama club and the football team working in Wallace's yard?
2. How does Trudi find out Wallace is planning to work in his yard on Saturday?
3. When does Wallace witness the instant Cavanaugh became his ex-best friend?
4. Explain why Coach Wrigley likes Wallace.
5. How does Mr. Fogelman's character change?
6. Name at least four more problems that plague the play in the last days.
7. Name some great last-minute ideas the kids have for the play.
8. What is the sixth act of vandalism on the play?
9. What incriminating evidence is found on the stage?
10. Who is the one drama club member who does not jump to the conclusion of blaming Wallace?
11. What does Mr. Fogelman do to Wallace?

Pages 151–180

1. How many tickets were sold to the play?
2. What do the cast and crew members decide to change at the last minute?

All rights reserved

3. Where does the author get the title for the book?

4. Why does Wallace decide to break the rules and go to the play performance?

5. Whom does Wallace first suspect?

6. What does Rick get from his locker?

7. How do Wallace and Rick discover the identity of the real culprit?

8. How does the real culprit sabotage the play?

9. How does Rachel react when Old Shep explodes?

10. Whom does Rachel think ruined the play?

11. How does Rachel realize she really likes Wallace?

12. Name at least two reasons why Wallace should be angry with Rachel.

All rights reserved

 © Novel Units, Inc.

Metaphors and Similes

A **metaphor** is a comparison between two unlike objects. For example, "he was a human tree." A **simile** is a comparison between two unlike objects that uses the words *like* or *as*. For example, "the color of her eyes was like the cloudless sky."

Directions: Complete the chart below by listing metaphors and similes from the novel, as well as the page numbers on which they are found. Identify metaphors with an "M" and similes with an "S." Translate the comparisons in your own words, and then list the objects being compared.

Metaphors/Similes	Ideas/Objects Being Compared
1. Translation:	
2. Translation:	
3. Translation:	

All rights reserved

Name _____

No More Dead Dogs
Activity #11 • Character Analysis
Use During and After Reading

Feelings

Directions: Choose a character from the book and complete the chart below.

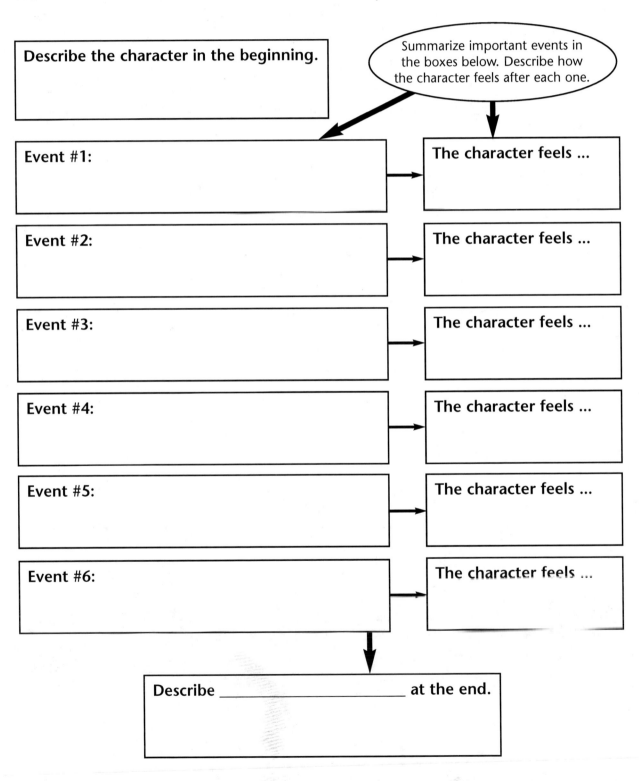

Describe the character in the beginning.

Summarize important events in the boxes below. Describe how the character feels after each one.

Event #1:   The character feels ...
Event #2:   The character feels ...
Event #3:   The character feels ...
Event #4:   The character feels ...
Event #5:   The character feels ...
Event #6:   The character feels ...

Describe _____ at the end.

Describe _____ at the end.

All rights reserved
© Novel Units, Inc.

Understanding Values

Values represent people's beliefs about what is important, good, or worthwhile. For example, most families value spending time together.

Directions: Think about the following characters from the novel and the values they exhibit. What do they value? What beliefs do they have about what is important, good, or worthwhile? On the chart below, list what each character values at the beginning of the novel, then list something else valued as the story progresses, and last list what each character values most by the end of the novel.

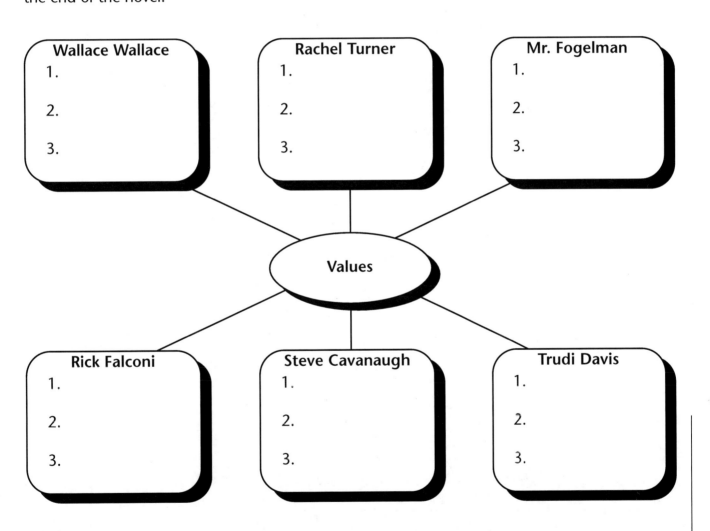

Which characters change their values as the novel progresses? Which characters do not change? Choose one character and write a paragraph explaining why you would most like to be like this character or why you would not want to be like this character.

All rights reserved

Story Pyramid

Directions: Using the pyramid, write words or phrases to summarize the story.

Line 1: One word that gives the setting

Line 2: Two words that identify the two main characters (in order of their appearance)

Line 3: Three words that explain the problem

Line 4: Two words that describe character #1; two words that describe character #2

Line 5: Two characters that interact with character #1; three characters that interact with character #2

Line 6: Six words that explain the resolution of the conflict

Line 7: Seven words that summarize your impression of the book

1 _____

2 _____ _____

3 _____ _____ _____

4 _____ _____ _____ _____

5 _____ _____ _____ _____ _____

6 _____ _____ _____ _____ _____ _____

7 _____ _____ _____ _____ _____ _____ _____

All rights reserved

Conflict

The **conflict** of a story is the struggle between two people or two forces. There are three main types of conflict: person vs. person, person vs. nature or society, and person vs. self.

Directions: The characters experience some conflicts in the story. In the chart below, list the names of three major characters. In the space provided, list a conflict each character experiences. Then explain how each conflict is resolved in the story.

Character:

Conflict	Resolution

Character:

Conflict	Resolution

Character:

Conflict	Resolution

All rights reserved

Theme

Directions: Design an original T-shirt that reflects one of the themes or major elements of the novel. Choose one of the following words: Friendship, Honesty, Humor, Talent, Creativity, or Stereotype. Use this word on the front of the T-shirt. On the back, create an original related slogan that applies to the novel.

Word on the front of the T-shirt _____

Slogan on the back of the T-shirt _____

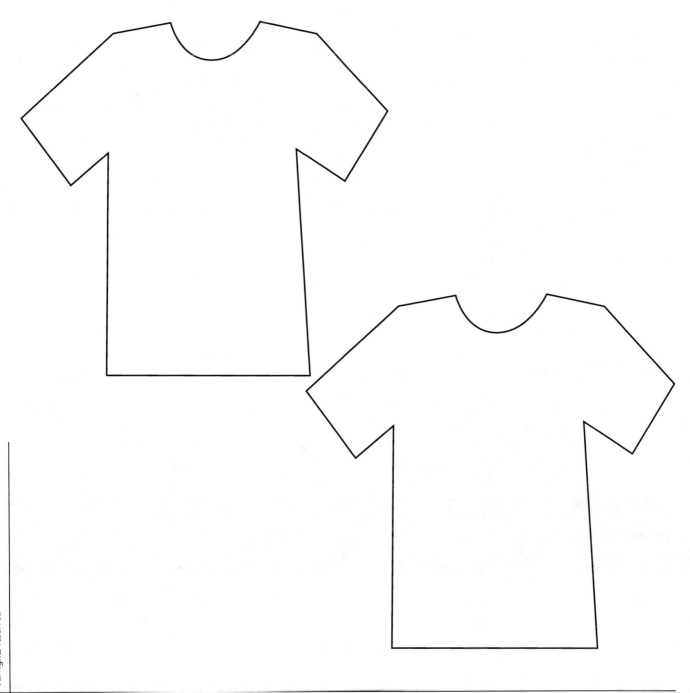

All rights reserved

Point of View

Directions: Choose one event from the novel. Write it in the center oval. Briefly tell about that event from each of the four given characters' points of view in the boxes provided. Choose another character and briefly tell the event from his or her point of view on the bottom lines.

Wallace

Rachel

EVENT

Mr. Fogelman

Rick

_____

_____

_____

_____

_____

_____

All rights reserved

Name _____

A. Identification: Match each of the following characters with the correct description.

____ 1. Mr. Fogelman	a.	sometimes mixes up his words
____ 2. Coach Wrigley	b.	fifth-grader who idolizes Wallace
____ 3. Rachel Turner	c.	actor who takes drama too seriously
____ 4. Wallace Wallace	d.	believes himself to be the best football player
____ 5. Steve Cavanaugh	e.	once produced an off-Broadway play
____ 6. Trudi Davis	f.	reporter who needs to get his facts straight
____ 7. Nathaniel Spitzner	g.	actress who takes drama very seriously
____ 8. Dylan Turner	h.	knows he's not a great football player
____ 9. Rick Falconi	i.	has a crush on Wallace
____ 10. Parker Schmidt	j.	Feather's father

B. True/False: Write a T beside the statement if it is true and an F beside the statement if it is false.

____ 11. Wallace's father died in a car accident before he was born.

____ 12. Wallace gives an unfavorable review of *Old Shep, My Pal* because he does not like his English teacher.

____ 13. Wallace cannot attend football practice as long as he is serving Mr. Fogelman's detention.

____ 14. Trudi has a crush on Rick Falconi.

____ 15. Mr. Fogelman assigns play practice detention to Wallace because he thinks it will inspire Wallace to write a better book report.

____ 16. Wallace persuades his football team friends to help him paint the backyard fence.

____ 17. Cavanaugh is rude to Wallace because Wallace was the one who happened to make the winning touchdown in the county championship game.

____ 18. Parker's story claims that Wallace refuses to play football until his English teacher raises his grade.

____ 19. The football team vandalizes the play set in revenge for Mr. Fogelman placing Wallace in detention.

____ 20. Wallace despises the drama club and wants nothing to do with the play.

____ 21. Dylan tries to get his sister to use her influence with Mr. Fogelman to get Wallace out of detention.

____ 22. Rachel confides her innermost thoughts in letters to Julia Roberts.

____ 23. Trudi supports her friend Rachel and accuses Wallace of sabotaging the play.

All rights reserved

Name _____

Multiple Choice: Choose the BEST answer.

_____ 1. What is NOT a reason Wallace helps the actors with their lines?
   a. He is bored.
   b. It is so easy.
   c. He enjoys it.
   d. He is making up for writing a bad review.

_____ 2. In Rachel's letters to Julia Roberts, what actor does she compare to Wallace?
   a. Brad Pitt
   b. Mel Gibson
   c. Johnny Depp
   d. Orlando Bloom

_____ 3. What does Wallace tell Mr. Fogelman is the biggest problem with the play?
   a. The actors are all amateurs.
   b. The set design needs more color.
   c. The play is all dialogue and no action.
   d. The gym is not big enough for rehearsals.

_____ 4. What is the third act of vandalism to the play?
   a. Old Shep is stolen.
   b. The moped has a blowout.
   c. A bucket of pepper drops on the actors.
   d. Ice water is thrown on the actors during rehearsal.

_____ 5. Why does Mr. Fogelman choose to do the play Wallace's way?
   a. Wallace has experience with acting off-Broadway.
   b. The cast responds to his ideas with lots of enthusiasm.
   c. Rachel refuses to be in the play unless Wallace has a say.
   d. The principal asks Mr. Fogelman to let Wallace work on the play.

_____ 6. Why does Wallace give Parker a news tip that the principal is looking into the vandalism?
   a. Wallace wants the publicity.
   b. Principal Chechik asks Wallace to do it.
   c. Wallace thinks Parker is the guilty person.
   d. Wallace hopes the bad guy will read the story and back off.

All rights reserved

_____ 7. Why does Wallace ask Laszlo Tamas to ride the moped?
     a. Laszlo owns a moped.
     b. Laszlo's father owns a Harley.
     c. Laszlo has his driver's license.
     d. Laszlo is the only cast member who can pass Mr. Fogelman's class.

_____ 8. In what role does Wallace cast Rory Piper?
     a. the dogcatcher
     b. Old Shep's trainer
     c. a Rollerblade instructor
     d. the Lamont children's father

_____ 9. What is the worst thing that happens when someone pours pancake syrup into Mr. Fogelman's filing cabinet?
     a. The filing cabinet is upside down.
     b. The *Old Shep, My Pal* files are damaged.
     c. The lock is broken on Mr. Fogelman's door.
     d. All the costumes are sticky and must be washed.

_____ 10. Why do the Dead Mangoes want to be in the play?
     a. They want to Rollerblade and ride mopeds.
     b. They want to do a rock and roll soundtrack.
     c. They are best friends with Nathaniel Spitzner.
     d. They are looking for a drummer for their band.

All rights reserved

© Novel Units, Inc.

Name _____

A. Short Answer: Briefly explain why each of these characters could be a suspect in the case of the play vandalism. Use evidence from the novel to support your answer.

1. Wallace—

2. Cavanaugh—

3. Giants football team—

4. Name another character and why he/she might want to sabotage the play.

B. Fill in the Blanks

5. The drama club members go to _____ on Saturday.

6. Rick and the other team members give Wallace _____ from last Saturday.

7. Mr. Fogelman plays _____ for the Dead Mangoes.

8. Mr. Fogelman prints _____ for the cast.

9. _____ is missing from the office.

10. The one word on the back of the jersey is _____.

11. Everyone but _____ assumes Wallace is guilty.

12. Wallace's last suggestion for the play is _____.

13. _____ thinks Wallace will join the Giants' team again.

14. Wallace believes someone planted the jersey to _____ him.

15. Rachel shocks the team on the football field by _____.

16. _____ suggests that Rachel simply ask Wallace if he is guilty.

All rights reserved

Name _____

Short Answer: Respond to the following questions on a separate sheet of paper.

1. Why do the cast and crew members decide to change the ending of the play on performance night?

2. What does the crew chant when they decide to change the play's ending?

3. Why does Wallace find it upsetting that the football team members attend the play performance?

4. Why doesn't Rachel turn in Wallace when she discovers him at the performance?

5. To what does Wallace compare hearing his dialogue on stage?

6. Why does Wallace suspect Rick as the culprit?

7. Why does Rick want to take photos of the performance?

8. Why does Dylan sabotage the play?

9. How does Wallace try to save the play?

10. How does the audience react to the unconventional play?

11. Why does Wallace tell a lie when he has never done so before?

12. How does Julia Roberts know that Rachel is "crazy about this guy Wallace" (p. 177)?

All rights reserved

Name _____

A. Fact/Opinion: Write an **F** before the statements that are fact and an **O** before the statements that are opinion.

_____ 1. Wallace's jersey is found among the shredded pieces of the script.

2. Football players are not good actors.

_____ 3. In all novels that have a dog on the cover, the dog dies.

_____ 4. The Giants are having a losing season.

_____ 5. *Old Shep, My Pal* is a play based on a great book by Zack Paris.

_____ 6. Wallace is holding out for a better English grade from Mr. Fogelman.

_____ 7. Rachel discovers she really likes Wallace.

_____ 8. Parker prints that Trudi and Wallace have a secret romance.

_____ 9. The Giants lose every game because Wallace is in detention.

_____ 10. Julia Roberts thinks Rachel likes Wallace.

B. Cause/Effect: Briefly explain what happens as a result of each of the following incidents.

11. Wallace writes a book report that Mr. Fogelman doesn't like.

12. Wallace spends detention at play practice.

13. Parker writes a story about Wallace's detention without checking his facts.

14. Wallace makes the winning touchdown in the county championship game.

15. Wallace introduces the Dead Mangoes to the play members.

All rights reserved

16. Rachel shares her innermost secrets in letters to Julia Roberts.

17. Laszlo has his driver's license.

18. Wallace uses the excuse that he cannot go to the fair with Trudi because he has to work in his yard.

19. Mr. Fogelman mellows out.

20. Wallace does not follow Mr. Fogelman's rules and comes to the play performance anyway.

C. Sequence: Number the events below in the order they occurred on performance night.

_____ 21. Dylan sabotages Old Shep.

_____ 22. Wallace jumps on the toy dog with a pillow.

_____ 23. Wallace lies to Rachel.

_____ 24. Rick spots the culprit on the football videotape.

_____ 25. Rick leaves his seat unnoticed.

_____ 26. Wallace realizes many of the Giants are attending the performance.

_____ 27. Wallace sees a sneaker sticking out from behind a curtain.

_____ 28. Rick pulls something suspicious from his locker.

_____ 29. The cherry bomb's wick is burning down as it rolls out on stage.

All rights reserved

 © Novel Units, Inc.

D. Identification: Match each of the following descriptions with the correct character.

____ 30. drummer for the Dead Mangoes

____ 31. mellows out to enjoy the new direction of the play

____ 32. whiny, obnoxious, and self-important

____ 33. realizes the football team is not a winning team

____ 34. a true actress who knows the show must go on

____ 35. author of *Old Shep, My Pal*

____ 36. Rollerblading wonder kid

____ 37. Bedford's only school reporter

____ 38. leader of the Dead Mangoes

____ 39. principal of Bedford Middle School

____ 40. brings out the best in people

____ 41. runs down Old Shep in the opening scene

____ 42. worships Wallace Wallace

____ 43. Mr. Good-Hair Day

____ 44. puts pepper on celery to mask its taste

____ 45. Wallace's true friend

____ 46. writes a letter to Rachel

____ 47. silly, shallow friend

____ 48. cast member who moves to California

____ 49. feeds the gang at the yard raking party

____ 50. saved by the crew to live another day

a. Rachel Turner

b. Joey Quick

c. the Void

d. Steve Cavanaugh

e. Mr. Chechik

f. Trudi Davis

g. Dylan Turner

h. Old Shep

i. Rory Piper

j. Coach Wrigley

k. Wallace Wallace

l. Rick Falconi

m. Leo Samuels

n. Zack Paris

o. Mr. Fogelman

p. Parker Schmidt

q. Laszlo Tamas

r. Julia Roberts

s. Mrs. Wallace

t. Nathaniel Spitzner

u. Feather Wrigley

E. Essay: Complete one of the following in a well-developed essay. Use specific evidence from the novel to support your answer.

a. Discuss the stereotypes of football players, drama club members, and teachers as presented in the novel and give examples of how one character breaks the stereotype.

b. Discuss Wallace's rule, honesty is the best policy, and how it applies to Wallace and at least one other character in the novel.

c. Choose one character and tell how that person is a true friend to Wallace.

All rights reserved

Answer Key

Activity #1: Answers will vary.

Activity #2: Answers will vary, but could include: football player—jock, stocky, tough, likes to win, athletic; actress—arrogant, glamorous, rich, beautiful, talented, popular; teacher—smart, stuffy, stubborn, always right, old-fashioned; reporter—wants the facts, good writer, inquisitive. (Bottom row) Wallace Wallace—not good at football, doesn't consider himself a hero, learns to like drama; Rachel Turner—is talented, believes the show must go on; Mr. Fogelman—at first fits the stereotype, but later plays keyboard in a rock band, accepts Wallace's unorthodox suggestions for the play; Parker Schmidt—is a good writer, but prints whatever he wants, doesn't check facts, stretches the truth

Activity #3: Answers will vary.

Activity #4: Nouns—reverie, calisthenics, ruckus, snarl; Verbs—mulling, mobbed, chortled, hyperventilating; Adjective—uncanny; Sentences will vary.

Activity #5: 1. reign 2. crimson 3. pandemonium 4. affable 5. queasy 6. strident 7–10. Answers will vary.

Activity #6: (Definitions to read in random order) bellowed—cried out loudly; sourly—unpleasantly; skulking—lurking about in a stealthy manner; clambered—climbed; snickered—laughed in a sly manner; perplexed—puzzled; ominously—in a sinister way; retorted—answered with a cutting reply; raved—talked enthusiastically; peevishly—crossly; barged—rudely entered; corridor—hallway; ricocheted—rebounded; bickering—quarreling; cringe—to draw back from something painful

Activity #7: plagued—troubled; fixated—all eyes focused on something; flailing—throwing about; urgent—imperative; mayhem—disorder, confusion; propel—push forward; savored—enjoyed; stricken—affected by something painful; sneer—smile with contempt; auburn—reddish brown; pathetic—pitiful; wheedle—coax; flustered—opposite of composed

Activity #8: Answers will vary, but could include:
hero
dauntless, gallant
worshipped, respected, admired
model, courage, quitter, chicken
cowering, whining, running
fearful, scared
coward

Activity #9: Answers will vary.

Study Guide
Pages 1–19: 1. honesty (p. 2) 2. *Old Shep, My Pal* by Zack Paris (p. 4) 3. because he knew Old Shep was going to die before he ever started reading the book (p. 5) 4. Bedford Middle School (p. 6) 5. his ex-best friend Steve Cavanaugh (p. 7) 6. He has to paint the garage door (p. 9). 7. actress Julia Roberts (p. 11) 8. *Old Shep, My Pal* (p. 14) 9. He tells Wallace that he had missed the meaning, the themes, and the great characters in the novel (p. 17). 10. Dylan sees Rachel and Trudi leave the gym with Wallace, who is a football hero to the ten year old boy (p. 19).

Pages 20–45: 1. write a serious paper giving reasons why Wallace doesn't like the book (p. 21) 2. his attitude (p. 22). 3. his mouth (p. 23) 4. fact checker (p. 28) 5. a career-ending injury, a personality conflict between Wallace and the coach, and Wallace is too good to play for a middle school team (p. 29) 6. "Old Shep, Dead Mutt" (p. 32) 7. Wallace (p. 32) 8. thinking up better dialogue for the play, standing up to Mr. Fogelman, his haircut, his voice, his double name, his posture, how

All rights reserved

everybody looks up to him, and his shoelaces (pp. 41–43) 9. Nathaniel Spitzner (p. 42) 10. All the wires on the set are tied in a huge knot hanging four feet above center stage (p. 44)

Pages 46–70. 1. four touchdowns (p. 47) 2. on the bench (p. 48) 3. wash the car (p. 49) 4. "someone who doesn't like Old Shep, My Pal, has a grudge against Mr. Fogelman, and spends a lot of time in the gym" (p. 50) 5. conducts a survey (p. 51) 6. He is bored, and it is easy (p. 52). 7. to destroy the play as revenge for getting kicked off the team (p. 53) 8. New York to see a play (pp. 54–55) 9. Brad Pitt (p. 55) 10. a yo-yo (p. 56) 11. The play doesn't show the most exciting event, Old Shep getting run over by the motorcycle (pp. 58–59). 12. Wallace is going to be honest and tell the truth no matter what. Other teachers have tried for a long time to make him do things their way and failed (p. 63). 13. A bucket of pepper is rigged to fall on the cast members (p. 67). 14. He helps pull students off the stage away from the pepper and catches Nathaniel when he falls off the stage (p. 68).

Pages 71–97: 1. Rachel's brother Dylan is sitting near him when his disguise is removed (p. 72). 2. Cavanaugh is talking to Wallace, but his intended audience is the team (p. 74). 3. a two-pound box of black pepper (p. 74) 4. Feather says the pepper is to disguise the taste of the celery (p. 75). 5. Cavanaugh, who would do anything to keep Wallace off the team (p. 76) 6. the eyes and ears of the school, top-secret, undercover spy, "professional rat" (p. 78) 7. help him spread Lawn-Gro on the grass (pp. 79–80) 8. two (p. 80) 9. to ride the moped that hits Old Shep, because he is the only one in the school who has his driver's license (pp. 81–82) 10. Harold Schwartzbaum, because he sneezed in class, and pepper can make a person sneeze (p. 85) 11. his ability to Rollerblade (p. 87) 12. as a Rollerblading dogcatcher (p. 88) 13. Someone pours pancake syrup over Mr. Fogelman's files on Old Shep, My Pal (p. 89). 14. Everyone loves it, including Rachel and Mr. Fogelman (p. 91). 15. a teen rock band who contacts Wallace, not Mr. Fogelman, about being a part of the play (pp. 95–97)

Pages 98–122: 1. Wallace (p. 98) 2. He releases Wallace from detention, even though Wallace has not written a proper review of Old Shep, My Pal (p. 102). 3. one month (p. 102) 4. He likes her smile, and she speaks her mind (p. 103). 5. Someone rolls marbles onto the stage during rehearsal to trip the actors on Rollerblades (pp. 104–105). 6. the entire Giants football team (p. 105) 7. He quits the football team and goes back to work on the play (p. 107). 8. She tells Parker that she is Wallace's girlfriend (p. 111). 9. He turns her dialogue into rap (p. 118). 10. He is going to play keyboard for the rock band the Dead Mangoes (pp. 119–120). 11. to rake leaves in Wallace's yard (pp. 121–122)

Pages 123–150: 1. The drama club members are more organized, and they were not invited; they just show up because they want to help Wallace (p. 124). 2. Wallace will not lie to Trudi or tell her he does not want to go with her to the fair on Saturday, so he uses working in the yard as an excuse (p. 125). 3. He sees the videotape of the locker scene from the championship game in the coach's office and sees Cavanaugh's expression after the game (p. 129). 4. Coach tells Wallace that he brings out the best in people (p. 130). 5. He mellows out by dressing more casually, frowning less and smiling more, and accepting the kids' ideas more (p. 134). 6. A busted skylight allows rain to warp the set, the remote-control car stops working, Leo and his family move to California, spotlights burn out, wasps invade the set, students get the flu, a toilet floods the gym floor, and Leticia throws up (p. 135). 7. Set designers make it look like real rain onstage, Wallace recruits the Old Shep Dancers, the band wires extra speakers for better sound, and the rebuilt Lamont house is fantastic (pp. 135–136). 8. Someone shreds the new copies of the script (p. 139). 9. Wallace's football jersey (p. 139) 10. Rachel (pp. 140–143) 11. He bans Wallace from rehearsals and the performance (p. 141).

Pages 151–180: 1. 714 (p. 152) 2. to take Wallace's advice and let Old Shep live (p. 153) 3. It is the chant from the crew who want Old Shep to live in the end (p. 154). 4. He is afraid someone will try to ruin the performance, and he wants to catch him or her (p. 156). 5. Rick (pp. 160–161) 6. a disposable camera (p. 163) 7. They watch a videotape of the locker room celebration in slow motion

All rights reserved

(pp. 165–166). 8. by putting a cherry bomb on the toy dog as it goes back onstage for the final scene (p. 168) 9. She tells the cast that "The show must go on!" (p. 170). 10. Rick (p. 172) 11. Julia Roberts writes Rachel a short note in her own handwriting telling Rachel she is crazy about Wallace (p. 177). 12. Rachel punches him and treats him like he is guilty (pp. 177–178).

Note: Answers to Activities #10–16 will vary. Suggested answers are given where applicable.
Activity #10: Answers will vary.

Activity #11: Suggestions for Wallace—He is totally honest about everything he says and does, and wants more than anything to play football with his friends. Event #1: He gives his honest opinion of the novel *Old Shep, My Pal*. He feels that Mr. Fogelman is unfair. Event #2: Mr. Fogelman gives Wallace detention. He feels he has been cheated of his afternoons practicing football. Event #3: He starts offering suggestions to improve the play. He feels compelled to tell the drama students and Mr. Fogelman what he honestly believes needs changing. Event #4: His football friends start to shun him. He feels upset because he thought they were his true friends. Event #5: The play is a smashing success thanks to Wallace. He feels elated that the drama students think he has helped them. Event #6: He lies to everyone about sabotaging the play. He feels bad about lying but is glad that he protected Rachel's feelings. At the end, Wallace realizes who his true friends really are—the ones who stick by him even when things go wrong.

Activity #12: Wallace Wallace—1. playing football 2. telling the truth 3. having friends who stick by you; Rachel Turner—1. acting 2. following the drama coach 3. defending her friends; Mr. Fogelman— 1. good literature 2. doing a play his way 3. letting students have fun; Rick Falconi—1. winning at football 2. helping Wallace 3. keeping Wallace's friendship; Steve Cavanaugh—1. looking good 2. his status in football 3. sarcasm with Wallace; Trudi Davis—1. impressing people 2. fitting in 3. being popular. Wallace, Rachel, Mr. Fogelman, and Rick change by the end of the novel, but Steve and Trudi remain the same.

Activity #13: Suggestion: Line 1—School; Line 2—Wallace, Rachel; Line 3—He gets detention; Line 4—honest, sincere, stubborn, indignant; Line 5—Rick, Steve, Mr. Fogelman, Trudi, Dylan; Line 6— Honest suggestions make a better play; Line 7—True friends always stick by each other.

Activity #14: Wallace: conflict with Mr. Fogelman who gives him detention; resolution—Wallace uses his time in detention to make the play better. Wallace: conflict with Steve after Wallace becomes the football hero; resolution—Wallace tries to be friendly with Steve. Wallace: conflict with the football players who want him to go against his principles to play football; resolution—He sticks with his principles, eventually helps the play, gets out of detention, and is back on the team. Wallace: conflict with Rachel who thinks he is sabotaging the play; resolution—He helps the drama members, catches the culprit, and protects Rachel from the truth about Dylan. Rachel: conflict with herself about her attitude toward Wallace; resolution—She learns to trust him, and they become friends. Dylan: conflict with the drama club because he vandalizes the play; resolution—He is caught and feels remorse, but doesn't destroy the play.

Activities #15–16: Answers will vary.

Quiz #1: A. 1. e 2. j 3. g 4. h 5. d 6. i 7. c 8. b 9. a 10. f **B.** 11. F (p. 3) 12. F (p. 4) 13. T (p. 22) 14. F (pp. 12–17) 15. T (p. 16) 16. F (p. 20) 17. T (p. 27) 18. T (p. 31) 19. F (pp. 33–39) 20. F (pp. 35–36) 21. T (pp. 38–39) 22. T (pp. 11, 37) 23. F (pp. 40–44)

Quiz #2: 1. d (p. 52) 2. a (p. 55) 3. c (p. 58) 4. c (p. 67) 5. b (p. 68) 6. d (p. 76) 7. c (p. 82) 8. a (p. 88) 9. b (p. 89) 10. b (pp. 96–97)

Quiz #3: A. 1. Wallace doesn't like the novel (p. 4); Mr. Fogelman gives him detention for a bad review (p. 5); he is not able to play football (p. 8); his jersey is found with the shredded scripts

All rights reserved

(pp. 139–140). 2. Cavanaugh has a grudge against Wallace for getting more attention after the championship game (p. 129). 3. The football team is not winning any games, and they blame Wallace for the losses (p. 129). 4. Parker Schmidt might want a juicy story for his newspaper; Mr. Fogelman might want to regain control of his play; Dylan might want his hero to play football again. **B.** 5. Wallace's house (p. 124) 6. the game ball (p. 131) 7. keyboard (p. 132) 8. new scripts (p. 138) 9. the paper shredder (p. 139) 10. Wallace (p. 140) 11. Rachel (pp. 142–143) 12. "Old Shep shouldn't die" (p. 142). 13. Dylan (p. 143) 14. frame (p. 145) 15. catching the football (p. 147) 16. Cavanaugh (pp. 149–150)

Quiz #4: 1. They have a great play because of Wallace and feel they owe it to him (p. 152). 2. "No more dead dogs! No more dead dogs!" (p. 154) 3. He still thinks one or more of the team is guilty of the vandalism and is afraid they may sabotage the performance (pp. 156–157). 4. because she trusts him (p. 157) 5. making the winning touchdown (p. 159) 6. because Rick leaves his seat, goes to his locker, and takes something out that looks suspicious (pp. 161–162) 7. Rick wants to give them to his good friend Wallace because Wallace is not allowed at the performance. Rick hopes it will patch their friendship (p. 163). 8. He is angry with Wallace for leaving the football team. He thinks that if he can get Wallace blamed for the incidents, Mr. Fogelman will dismiss him from the play and he will have to return to the football team (p. 168). 9. He jumps on the toy dog armed with a cherry bomb and tries to muffle the explosion with a pillow (pp. 169–170). 10. They think it is great and give it a standing ovation (pp. 171–172). 11. He wants to protect Rachel from knowing that the person sabotaging the play is her little brother Dylan (p. 173). 12. Rachel has been writing to Julia Roberts for some time talking about Wallace and dropping hints, even though Rachel is not even aware of it herself (p. 177).

Novel Test: A. 1. F 2. O 3. O 4. F 5. O 6. O 7. F 8. F 9. O 10. F **B.** 11. Mr. Fogelman gives Wallace detention (p. 5). 12. Wallace begins to make suggestions to change (or improve, according to Wallace) the play (pp. 34–35). 13. Many students believe Parker's story and blame Wallace for the team's bad season and the vandalism to the play (p. 34). 14. The town thinks he is a football hero, and he loses his friend Cavanaugh (pp. 6–7). 15. Mr. Fogelman joins the band as a keyboard player (p. 120). 16. Julia Roberts answers Rachel's letters and tells Rachel she is crazy about Wallace (p. 177). 17. He gets to drive the moped in the opening scene of the play (p. 82). 18. Trudi gets the entire drama club to come to Wallace's house on Saturday morning and clean the yard (pp. 123–125). 19. The cast and crew enjoy working on the play more and do a better job (pp. 134–135). 20. He and Rick finally discover who the real culprit is behind all the vandalism (pp. 166–167). **C.** 21. 6 22. 8 23. 9 24. 4 25. 2 26. 1 27. 5 28. 3 29. 7 **D.** 30. c 31. o 32. t 33. j 34. a 35. n 36. i 37. p 38. b 39. e 40. k 41. q 42. g 43. d 44. u 45. l 46. r 47. f 48. m 49. s 50. h **E.** Answers will vary. Refer to the scoring rubric on page 36 of this guide.

All rights reserved

Linking Novel Units® Student Packets to National and State Reading Assessments

During the past several years, an increasing number of students have faced some form of state-mandated competency testing in reading. Many states now administer state-developed assessments to measure the skills and knowledge emphasized in their particular reading curriculum. This Novel Units® guide includes open-ended comprehension questions that correlate with state-mandated reading assessments. The rubric below provides important information for evaluating responses to open-ended comprehension questions. Teachers may also use scoring rubrics provided for their own state's competency test.

Scoring Rubric for Open-Ended Items

3-Exemplary	Thorough, complete ideas/information Clear organization throughout Logical reasoning/conclusions Thorough understanding of reading task Accurate, complete response
2-Sufficient	Many relevant ideas/pieces of information Clear organization throughout most of response Minor problems in logical reasoning/conclusions General understanding of reading task Generally accurate and complete response
1-Partially Sufficient	Minimally relevant ideas/information Obvious gaps in organization Obvious problems in logical reasoning/conclusions Minimal understanding of reading task Inaccuracies/incomplete response
0-Insufficient	Irrelevant ideas/information No coherent organization Major problems in logical reasoning/conclusions Little or no understanding of reading task Generally inaccurate/incomplete response

All rights reserved

 © Novel Units, Inc.